ॐ

KRISHNA ROCKS

by

Nishita Chaitanya

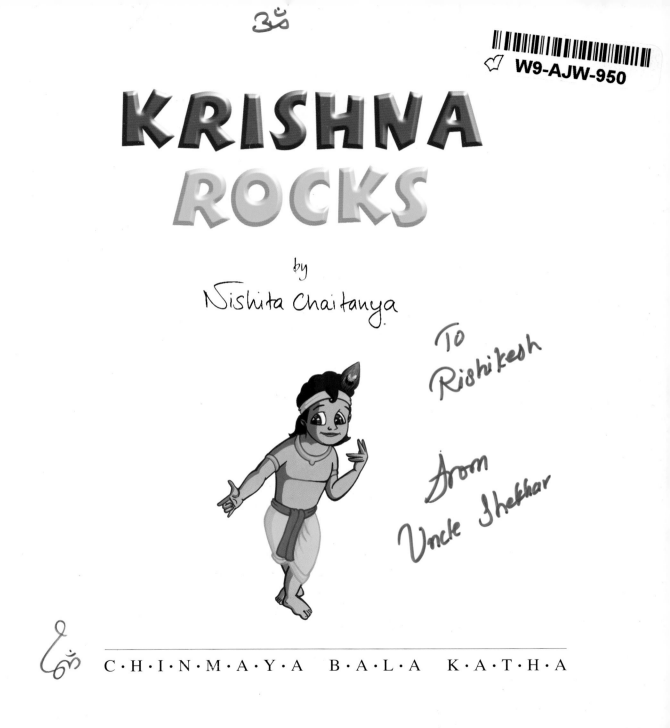

C·H·I·N·M·A·Y·A B·A·L·A K·A·T·H·A

It was a new day bursting with sunshine. Krishna was sitting on his porch.

Krishna was a small and lovable blue boy, with curly black hair, and a twinkle in his big brown eyes. He had a naughty little smile, which made dimples in his cute, chubby cheeks.

As he sat on the porch, a brightly coloured beautiful butterfly landed on Krishna's hand.

Everyone and everything wanted to be near Krishna. He had a special way of making everyone feel so happy. **He made people feel nice and warm, just like we feel when we get a big bear hug.**

Everyone was up early that morning.

Krishna could hear pots and pans - *clink clink*. He could hear sweeping and cleaning - *swish swish*. He could hear chitter and chatter - *buzz buzz*.

There seemed much excitement in Brindaavan that morning. The adults were all very busy.

"Hmmm, what are they doing?" thought Krishna. Just then he saw his father coming out of the house in fancy new clothes.

"Is it someone's birthday? Is there going to be a party?" asked curious little Krishna.

"No, not a party, but there'll still be lots of food. Yummy food, just the kind you like," said his very affectionate father, Nanda Baba.

"How come?" asked cute little Krishna.

"Well, son, we are getting ready for the big prayer function."

"Oh! Whom are we praying to? What are we praying for?" asked sweet little Krishna.

"We are praying to Lord Indra, the Lord of rain, so that he may send us rain this year."

"But why do you have to pray for rain?" asked Krishna, now looking a little puzzled.

Nanda Baba replied: "The rain makes the green grass grow. And our gentle brown cows like eating green grass. The more they eat, the bigger they become. The bigger they become, the more milk they make. The more milk they make, the more milk we get. The more milk we get, the more butter we make. Then, we take the butter to sell and we make money!"

Krishna thought about it: "The rain is for the grass, the grass is for the cows, the cows are for the milk, the milk is for the butter, and butter is for money."

Krishna looked at his father with his big brown eyes, jumped up and asked, "So, we're praying for money?"

"Well... er... son," said Nanda Baba, trying to think of a good answer, "if we pray to Indra, he will be happy with us and give us rain."

Krishna's cute little face became very thoughtful.

"Is Indra God?" asked Krishna.

"No, he's only the Lord of rain."

"What about God? Do we have to make him happy, too?"

Krishna's father was surprised to hear Krishna say this. His face also became thoughtful.

He knew his son was very special. Even though Krishna was only a little boy, he was very wise. He was very, VERY wise.

"I know a secret. I know how to make good things happen," said Krishna, his eyes wide with excitement.

"How, dear?" asked Nanda Baba.

"We do not have to pray to Indra for good things to happen to us. **We just have to <u>do</u> good things for good things to happen to us.**"

"Yes, you are right," said Krishna's proud father. "You are RIGHT!" And he swept up the little boy in his arms and hugged him tight.

"But now that we've made all the yummy food... what should we pray for?" wondered aloud Nanda Baba.

Krishna's soft cheeks made dimples as he smiled. His big brown eyes twinkled as he looked out at the cows.

"I know!" exclaimed Krishna. "**God gives us without our asking**. So let's pray to God and say 'thank you'. Thank you, thank you, thank you!

"Thank you, God, for the grass that grows. Thank you, God, for the cows that moo. Thank you, God, for the milk we drink. Thank you, God, for everything!"

"What a good idea," thought Nanda Baba. "What a very good idea. What a very, VERY good idea!

"Yes, this year we shall worship the cows for giving us milk, and the mountain for giving us grass. And not Indra!" said Nanda Baba.

The next day they all went to the Govardhana Mountain.

They wore shiny new clothes. They took lots of yummy food. They walked around the mountain singing sweet songs, and they danced, too.

In their hearts they thanked God for giving them the grass, and the sun, and the wind, and so many other wonderful things.

They washed the cows and made them clean. They placed new bells around the cows' necks. They also decorated them with flowers.

In their hearts they thanked God for the cows. The cows are so gentle and kind. The cows give and give. They never stop giving.

Indra was the Lord of rain. He was tall and strong. He was proud and pompous. He wanted people to pray to him. He wanted to feel important and powerful.

Every year the people of Brindaavan prayed to him. So this year he was waiting. He waited and waited. But there was no prayer. He waited some more. But then he couldn't wait any longer. He wanted to see what was happening.

He jumped on his big white flying elephant and *zoom!* flew to Brindaavan.

He was shocked! He saw the people worshipping the cows, and he became angry. He saw them worshipping the mountain, and he became very angry. He then saw them listening to Krishna, and he became very, VERY angry!

"Hmph! They're worshipping cows and a mountain instead of ME?" said Indra. "What? How dare they! I'll show them... .

"I'll make them sorry. I'll make them *soooooooooo* sorry!"

And so he sent rain, lots and LOTS of rain. He *huffed* and he *puffed*, he *mumbled* and he *grumbled*, and he worked up a terrible, terrible storm.

Indra howled, "Flood the grass! Sting the cows! How dare these people insult me!"

In Brindaavan, it started raining. It started pouring. Thunder crashed and lightning flashed. The wind blew hard. The wind blew cold. So cold, the rain became hail. And the hailstones scratched the cows as they hit them.

The rain went everywhere. It went through the windows, under the doors, over the gardens. It rained so much and so hard, the water flooded the houses and the barns. Everyone was wet.

Everyone was afraid. Everyone ran to Krishna.

"Krishna, please help us!" screamed a shivering little girl.

"Krishna, do something!" shouted a frightened little boy.

"Krishna, please save us from Indra's anger!" they all said together.

Krishna thought for a moment and said calmly, "Don't worry. Indra can't hurt us. We have worshipped the Govardhana Mountain, so it will help us."

Krishna walked towards the Govardhana Mountain. Everyone followed Krishna. They took along umbrellas, raincoats and blankets.

The moment Krishna reached Govardhana, he scooped up the mountain with one hand, as if he was picking up ice-cream!

He held up the mountain with his little pinkie finger. Govardhana looked like a big, BIG umbrella.

Everyone was amazed. "*Wow*!" they thought, "How can this tiny blue boy pick up such a huge mountain?"

Krishna's friends were all excited. They were thinking: "Krishna is the best! He is the strongest, bravest and kindest little boy. He is holding up this whole mountain with just one little finger!"

"Come stand underneath, you will be safe," Krishna called out.

Everyone looked at Krishna. He was so small. They looked at the mountain. The mountain was so big. They looked at Krishna again. And they looked at the mountain once more.

"I promise you the mountain will not fall," Krishna reassured them. One by one, everyone crawled underneath the mountain. One by one, the cows, followed.

And in their hearts they all thanked Krishna.

It rained everywhere, but not underneath the mountain. The wind blew everywhere, but not underneath the mountain. They were safe. Everything and everyone was safe. **Where Krishna was, all was safe.**

It rained and rained and rained. For seven days and seven nights it rained. Krishna held and held and held. For seven days and seven nights he held up the Govardhana Mountain with his little pinkie finger.

Krishna did not eat or sleep, he did not even take a break.

Krishna stood in the same spot with a loving smile on his face. He did not get tired, even after seven days and seven nights.

Finally the rain stopped. The skies became clear once again. The sun came out and dried the earth.

There were cheers and squeals of celebration. "The rain has stopped, the rain has stopped." The children danced around Krishna singing, **"You saved us, you saved us, Krishna, you saved us."**

Now everyone crawled out from underneath the mountain. They stretched. They smiled. They looked at Krishna and felt his magic. He made them feel nice and warm, just like we feel when we get a big bear hug. And once again in their hearts they all thanked Krishna.

The children followed their parents home. The calves followed the children home. Krishna waited patiently for everyone to leave.

Indra had stopped the rain because he saw
Krishna holding up the mountain. He knew
this could not be an ordinary person.

Indra thought, "Krishna looks small and
playful, but he is extremely powerful. I
wanted everyone to worship me. I got
angry when they didn't.

"But I was wrong. The grass should not
have been flooded. The cows should not
have been stung. The people should not
have been scared.

"I should apologise for my anger and my
arrogance."

Indra came down to the earth on his big white flying elephant just as Krishna was lowering the mountain.

Before Indra could say anything, Krishna looked at him and said, **"Our power should be used to help and serve people, not to hurt them!"**

Indra felt ashamed. He was in-charge of sending rain to help plants grow, so that he could help people.

He started enjoying his power and forgot about helping people. He wanted more and more power, and wanted people to see how great he was.

Krishna had even more power than Indra.

But **Krishna helped people. He did not hurt them with his power.**

It had rained and thundered and hailed for seven days and seven nights. But around Krishna it was always safe and still. He carried the load on his little pinkie finger with patience and a smile.

And everyone realised: Hey, Krishna ROCKS!

Are you helping people? There are so many ways to help them.

When we have more money, we can give it to others.
When we have toys, we can share them with other children.
When we know how to do a maths sum, we can teach other children.
When we learn a new game, we can show others how to play it.
Even though we may already have many friends, we can still be friends with a new child at school.

Whatever we have, remember to use it to help people.

Krishna is always helping. What about you?

Krishna is so kind. Are you?

Krishna makes people feel warm and nice.
Do you?

Krishna Rocks! Do you???